| July | August | September | October | Ember | December | |
|------|--------|-----------|---------|-------|----------|------|
|  |  |  | 1 |  |  | Mon |
|  |  |  | 2 |  |  | Tues |
|  | 1 |  | 3 |  |  | Wed |
|  | 2 |  | 4 | 1 |  | Thu |
|  | 3 |  | 5 P | 2 P |  | Fri |
|  | 4 | 1 | 6 | 3 | 1 | Sat |
| 1 | 5 | 2 | 7 | 4 | 2 | Sun |
| 2 | 6 | 3 | 8 | 5 | 3 | Mon |
| 3 | 7 | 4 | 9 | 6 | 4 | Tues |
| 4 | 8 | 5 | 10 | 7 | 5 | Wed |
| 5 | 9 | 6 | 11 | 8 | 6 | Thu |
| 6 | 10 P | 7 P | 12 | 9 | 7 | Fri |
| 7 | 11 | 8 | 13 | 10 | 8 | Sat |
| 8 | 12 | 9 | 14 | 11 | 9 | Sun |
| 9 | 13 | 10 | 15 | 12 | 10 | Mon |
| 10 | 14 | 11 | 16 | 13 | 11 | Tues |
| 11 | 15 | 12 | 17 | 14 | 12 | Wed |
| 12 | 16 | 13 | 18 | 15 | 13 | Thu |
| 13 P | 17 | 14 | 19 | 16 | 14 | Fri |
| 14 | 18 | 15 | 20 | 17 | 15 | Sat |
| 15 | 19 | 16 | 21 | 18 | 16 | Sun |
| 16 | 20 | 17 | 22 | 19 | 17 | Mon |
| 17 | 21 | 18 | 23 | 20 | 18 | Tues |
| 18 | 22 | 19 | 24 | 21 | 19 | Wed |
| 19 | 23 | 20 | 25 | 22 | 20 | Thu |
| 20 | 24 | 21 | 26 | 23 | 21 | Fri |
| 21 | 25 | 22 | 27 | 24 | 22 | Sat |
| 22 | 26 | 23 | 28 | 25 | 23 | Sun |
| 23 | 27 | 24 | 29 | 26 | 24 | Mon |
| 24 | 28 | 25 | 30 | 27 | 25 | Tues |
| 25 | 29 | 26 | 31 | 28 | 26 | Wed |
| 26 | 30 | 27 |  | 29 | 27 | Thu |
| 27 | 31 | 28 |  | 30 P | 28 P | Fri |
| 28 |  | 29 |  |  | 29 | Sat |
| 29 |  | 30 |  |  | 30 | Sun |
| 30 |  |  |  |  | 31 | Mon |
| 31 |  |  |  |  |  | Tues |
| **Grune** | **August** | **Spune** | **Sektober** | **Ember** | **December** | |

# DISCWORLD
# Ankh–Morpork
# Post Office
# Handbook
# Diary 2007

## PERSONAL DETAILS

Name: _____

Post Office Rank/Title: _____

_____

PO Badge No. (if applicable): _____

Postal Route (if applicable): _____

_____

List any Work-Related Injuries: _____

_____

_____

_____

Counter Number (if applicable): _____

Clacks 'Handle' (if applicable): _____

_____

Species: _____

Gender (if known): _____

Date of Birth: _____

Home Address (including Post Code – be careful

with spelling and write clearly): _____

_____

_____

_____

_____

_____

C-Mail address: _____

Previous Employment History: _____

_____

_____

Have you Walked the Walk? YES/NO

# A HISTORY OF THE ANKH-MORPORK POST

In days of yore (about 225 years before olden days, but about 200 years later than ancient times), the Kings of Ankh used messengers to take orders and other messages to all parts of the Sto Plains and far beyond.

The fastest messengers could achieve 200 miles in one day, with frequent changes of horse and cushion at staging, or relay, posts along the route. Riders tended to be young, and on the whole did not grow very old, partly because of the effects on the internal organs of days spent in the saddle of a galloping horse, but also because highwaymen were rife (which is worse than endemic but not quite as bad as ubiquitous). Guards were occasionally sent to flush them out, and there was a gibbet at each relay post to show possible robbers what their likely career prospects were.

And thus the word 'Post' came to be applied to the sending of the mail (the preferred 'Corpse Route' being judged a winner in terms of brand recognition but otherwise lacking in market appeal).

Only the King and certain approved officials, royal relatives, hangers-on and chums were permitted to send letters via the Royal Messenger Service, or Post Boys, but it was not unknown for rich merchants and others to come to private, and highly illegal, arrangement with the couriers.

In those days, the ordinary people of Ankh-Morpork had to rely on the good offices of traders and merchants to carry their mail for them as they journeyed around the Disc. This service was fairly reliable, but letters could take months to arrive, depending on the merchant's destination and the nature of the letter's contents. Merchants, like everyone else, need something entertaining to read of a night by the campfire, and a really good letter might spend years going up and down the trade routes before finally reaching its destination. Daisy's letter to Willie, telling him how much she was looking forward to him coming home from the wars, was on the Ankh-Morpork-Genua route for more than seven years; dozens of copies were made, and it became the subject of a series of postcards and a rather louche cabaret.

Unseen University set up its own postal service to handle the wizards' personal mail within the city. Owl Post had been tried, but A-M owls turned out to be brighter and less tractable than their rural counterparts, and regarded letters as a warm and easily obtainable nesting material. UU staff did their best to reclaim the post from precarious roosts, and they would eventually be delivered stamped 'Nested on by Owls', although this really did not need pointing out. When an owl has nested for any length of time on your mail, you know it has. You do not need it drawn to your attention.

In AM1530, King Cirone II established a formal network of messengers and horses along important routes, and he appointed a 'Master of the Posts' to administer the system, and to ensure that it worked to maximum efficiency. The first Master of the Posts was Sir Rolande de Colline, who had been a warrior-knight alongside the Assassins' Guild founder, Sir Gyles de Murfoote. This high-profile link helped to ensure that the Royal Mail Posts were not subject to attacks by would-be thieves. This system worked quite well, and the term Red Letter Day comes from the fact that the mail was often delivered stained with blood. On the other hand, it had arrived, which was an occasion for rejoicing.

By AM1635, King Lorenzo I (father of Lorenzo the Kind) had decided that that the general public could also use the King's Letter Office of Ankh-Morpork and the Sto Plains. The original building, sited on Broad Way, had become commonly known as the Post Office and its chief administrator was now called the Post Master. King Lorenzo dictated at the same time that all houses and properties in Ankh-Morpork should display a number, to facilitate the delivery of the post. There was some initial confusion, when people thought they could choose their own number, and for a while the city was full of Number Ones. In addition, no one wanted to be a Number Eight, that being considered unlucky. This confusion was cleared up in robust fashion when the King sent a squad to pull down every eighth house. Another relic of those days is that every property in Brewer Street is still numbered 34, but this is Traditional and thus considered quaint, not daft.

As the system established itself, all post on the Sto Plains using the Royal Mail had, by Royal Decree, to travel via Ankh-Morpork. This meant that, for example, a letter going from Sto Helit to Sto Lat (a distance of some five miles) would have to journey the twenty miles from Sto Helit into Ankh-Morpork, and a similar distance back again to Sto Lat. The Post Master at the time, Mr Jedediah Palmer, set up a system of new postal routes – called Cross-Posting – which meant mail did not have to travel via Ankh-Morpork. He also introduced the first mail coach service.

Legend has it that the reason for the original Decree has a lot to do with the King's paranoia, and the very large black kettle that even now can be found in the Central Post Office.

## MAIL COACHES

Highway robbery was (and still is) a major problem on the Sto Plains, and the old system of Post Boys left the mail, and its carriers, very vulnerable to attack. The passenger stage coaches fared little better, and travellers rarely arrived at their destinations with all their possessions – or even all their clothes. So Post Master Palmer set up a system of mail coaches, with a driver and an armed guard on each coach. In the first day of operation, four highwaymen were shot on sight by guards on the mail coaches.*

Flushed with success, Palmer tried other tactics, employing for the purpose a number of men with far more scars than teeth, and names like Charlie the Snake. They would travel on the stage disguised as passengers, waiting for an innocent (by comparison) thief to hold it up. A favourite disguise (who can say why?) was 'Governess Taking Three Innocent Young Ladies to Finishing School', but 'Humble Priest' and 'Apparently Drunk And Easy To Rob Elderly Gentleman' also achieved remarkable results . . . so remarkable, in fact, that the populations of entire villages would run away when they heard the coach coming. The new guards did not bother with finicky things like gallows, and generally delivered miscreants to the Post Master in a bucket.

After that, the mail was left alone, and the mail coaches became much more popular with passengers once they heard that 'Governess Taking Three Innocent Young Ladies to Finishing School' would no longer be travelling on that route.

*That is to say, they were men on horseback and apparently 'looked a bit funny' to the guards. One of them turned out to have documents on him suggesting that he was a travelling seller of patent medicines, but this was taken to be proof that highwaymen are terrible liars.

It was during the reign of Lorenzo the Kind that the Master of the Posts, Sir Henry Mark, came up with the system of stampings (which soon became known as 'postmarks') to enable him to time the progress of the mail through the city and beyond – he could then detect inefficient postal stages and slow-moving postal carriers.

Lorenzo the Kind embraced this management tool vigorously and, during the following ten months, the service improved tremendously, although eight tardy Post Boys and seven lazy Sub-Postmasters were hung, drawn and quartered, for the amusement of the citizens and, as Sir Henry said, 'Pour encourager les autres.' Word of mouth – not helped by the King's habit of speaking with his mouth full, plus his courtiers' understandable fear of the consequences of disobedience – transformed this to 'pour encourager les autriches' (ostriches) by the time it had reached Quirm, where the local postal staff immediately started to train these flightless birds to deliver the post in that city. This worked surprisingly well, although the new Post Birds did have a tendency to swallow any amusingly shaped packages. The Quirm Sub-Postmaster met with resistance when he tried to encourage his fellow Sub-Postmasters to use exotic birds as delivery tools. He resented their reactionary attitude and accused them of burying their heads in the sand.

## THE DARK AGES

Some hundred years ago, the Post Office began to go into a decline. This was shortly after the construction of the fine new building, conforming to the general rule that all organisations begin to fail the moment they take over a purpose-built headquarters. Success went to the Post Office's collective head. Despite having the most recognised and respected name of any city organisation, it was persuaded by seers and soothsayers to install expensive and untried equipment and change its name to PO!!!!!

People who knew how to do it all were paid to make way for much younger people who didn't know how to do anything at all, and therefore did it badly but much more cheaply. Staff left. The remaining staff worked harder. The new machinery failed to work. Morale fell. The cost of postage went up as efficiency plummeted. Coaches broke down and, as feed and staff bills remained unpaid, the coach drivers took the horses and vehicles in lieu of back pay.

The Post Office stumbled on for decades, but when Ankh-Morpork opened its gates to dwarf immigrants from the mountains, more than doubling the flow of people across the Sto Plains, many citizens took advantage of the dwarfs' informal but reliable couriers. For a while the Post Office maintained a city-wide service, but the End had Come.

## WEEKDAYS

### Offices in Ankh-Morpork

At the larger Post Offices the hours of business are, as a rule, from 8.30a.m. to 6p.m., or 6.30p.m., except on Public Holidays. Exceptionally, some Sub-offices close earlier on Saturdays. All classes of Postal and Clacks business are transacted at the Broad Way Post Office headquarters building between the hours of 8a.m. and 8p.m.

### Offices outside Ankh-Morpork

Larger Post Offices will be open from 9a.m. until 6p.m. Smaller local Post Offices may operate shorter hours – 9a.m. until 5.30p.m. All excepting Public Holidays. Local small Post Offices may also close early on one day of the week, generally on the local half-holiday.

## HOGSWATCH, PATRICIAN'S DAY AND OTHER PUBLIC HOLIDAYS

### Offices in Ankh-Morpork

The Broad Way Post Office will be open from 9.30a.m. until 12.30p.m. for all normal services, except for the sales of stamps of a face value of 2 dollars or more and for the acceptance of mail addressed to the Shades, to Borogravia, to Tezuman or to 36 Chitterling Street.

On Hogswatchday, there is one house-to-house delivery of letters and other postal packets within the city walls of Ankh-Morpork (excepting the Shades and 36 Chitterling Street).

Offices outside Ankh-Morpork:
Local Post Offices may open by local arrangement.

**Mail to 36 Chitterling Street:**
Letters to this address will be stored at the Central Post Office until this address reappears in conditions of sufficient stability to allow mail delivery to be attempted.

# POSTING BOXES

Members of the public should be aware that new Posting Boxes, now found on many streets, are (a) 6' high (b) painted red, and (c) furnished with a slot for the ingress of mail.

The Post Office **ACCEPTS NO RESPONSIBILITY** for letters posted into something that is merely 6' high OR red OR possessed of a slot. There have been regrettable Incidents.

**Note 1: Posting Box Mail Eaten by Snails.**

We regret that snails are colonising Posting Boxes in the damper parts of the city. Any mail recovered from these boxes may arrive at its destination marked 'Eaten By Snails'.

**Note 1(a):** The Ankh-Morpork Post Office does not accept that snails eat postage stamps only.

**Note 1(b):** Following further investigation, the Ankh-Morpork Post Office accepts that snails *are* particularly attracted to the 50p 'Cabbage Field' stamp. These stamps are being reprinted with a substance in the glue that is harmful to snails but in all probability harmless to humans.

**Note 1(c):** The Ankh-Morpork Post Office accepts that the new glue on the 50p 'Cabbage Field' stamp leaves an unpleasant aftertaste. Therefore, until further notice, purchasers of the 50p 'Cabbage Field' stamp will also receive one (1) Medium Strength Post Office Peppermint free and gratis.

**Note 1(d):** The Ankh-Morpork Post Office is pleased to announce that the incidence of snails in Posting Boxes should now be severely reduced due to the insertion of official Post Office Toads in all affected Posting Boxes.

**Note 1(e):** The Ankh-Morpork Post Office accepts that not everyone likes the taste of Peppermint, and therefore every customer entitled to a free Peppermint may opt instead for one (1) violet Jujube.

**Note 1(f):** The Ankh-Morpork Post Office regrets that measures taken to reduce the incidence of snails in Posting Boxes has resulted in some mail having to be stamped 'Dribbled On By Toads'. To deal with this problem we have taken on a number of Klatchian Melon Snakes.

**Note 1(g):** Those customers entitled to a Post Office Peppermint or Jujube (see notes 1(c) and 1(e)) may in special circumstances be offered one (1) Cherry-flavoured Cough Drop.

**Note 1(h):** The Ankh-Morpork Post Office regrets that the Klatchian Melon Snake is unfortunately easily confused with the deadly Banded Brown Rumba, even by our suppliers. However, quantities of the anti-venom have now been secured, and staff and customers who feel they might have been bitten should calmly proceed to any Post Office they are reasonably certain of reaching within three minutes.

**Note 1(i):** The Ankh-Morpork Post Office regrets that it has become necessary to stamp the mail from a few Posting Boxes with the words 'Snake Venom, Deadly on Contact, Open With Care'. To enable normal service to resume, a number of Posting Boxes are now home to specimens of the Howondaland Red Mongoose, which are totally harmless to humans and cannot possibly be confused with any dangerous breed of creature, even by the most short-sighted and culpable supplier.

**Note 1(j):** The Ankh-Morpork Post Office regrets that it has become necessary to stamp certain items of mail 'Defecated Upon By Mongeese'.

**Note 1(k):** The Ankh-Morpork Post Office has followed with interest the debate in the correspondence columns of *The Times* on the mongooses/mongeese controversy, but takes the view that this is not the point at issue. They still defecate, apparently almost continuously.

**Note 1(l):** The Ankh-Morpork Post Office regrets that it has had to stamp some mail: 'Found Being Used As Bedding By Hamsters', but wishes to point out that staff are almost certain hamsters have not been formally inserted into our Posting Boxes. We believe this is the work of a Prankster.

> **Note 1(l):** [Supplemental] The Ankh-Morpork Post Office takes similar views on the occurrence in our Posting Boxes of kittens, lizards, and Mr Edward Souser, 21, of 11 Pellicool Steps, apparently on his stag night.

**Note 1(m):** The Ankh-Morpork Post Office is please to announce that it is inviting gnomes and small gargoyles to take up residence in our Posting Boxes, a move which will increase the security of the service and make a valuable contribution to the housing stock of the city.

**Note 1(n):** The Ankh-Morpork Post Office regrets that, following the recent very high tide and flooding in the Rivergate area, it has had occasion to stamp some mail 'Nibbled By Unknown Marine Creatures'.

An official lobster has been acquired.

## MISCELLANEOUS REGULATIONS

All letters posted in Ankh-Morpork must carry the postage due for their intended destination in stamps approved by the Postmaster General. No other stamps are acceptable, no matter how pretty they are.

Letters posted in Ankh-Morpork for onward transmigration by the Semaphore or clacks must carry sufficient postage to cover overland travel at the destination. Tariffs are on display at all Post Offices.

All stamps issued by the Post Office remain valid at their face value for all time, provided that they remain legible. However, this does not apply to the Special Edition 50p Green 'Cabbage Field' stamp, **WHICH MUST NOT BE AFFIXED TO AN ENVELOPE**. This stamp has a gum derived from kohlrabi and cauliflower, intended to give expatriate customers a whiff of home. Regrettably, this has proved to be all too realistic.

It is believed, following the fumigation of the Post Office and four coaches, that the few remaining stamps are in sealed jars, in the hands of private collectors or the City Watch. Anyone in possession of such a stamp **SHOULD NOT TAKE IT TO THE POST OFFICE** but should instead arrange to meet a member of the staff in a suitable open space to hand it over in exchange for safe stamps to an equivalent value. **Do Not Lick It Or Allow It To Become Wet In Any Way**.

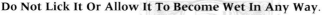

## LETTERS

### Weight and Size

There is no limit of weight. The limits of size are:

**Maximum:**

Two feet (2') in length, eighteen inches (18") in width and eighteen inches (18") in depth; or if made up in a roll, three feet three inches (3' 3") for the length and twice the diameter combined, and two feet six inches (2' 6") for the greatest dimension.

**Minimum:**

Envelopes less than four inches (4") in length by two and three-quarter inches (2 3/4") in width must not be used.

Eggs, fish, poultry, game, rabbits, meat, fruit and vegetables are not transmissible by Letter Post and certain articles may be sent only if specially packed (see 'Packing and Make-up' below).

Coupons, forms, cards and so on, bearing written answers to acrostics and guessing competitions, and written communications indicating, whether by means of words, marks, letters or numbers, moves in a game of Thud, are inadmissible.

Stationery, when sent not filled in to a person who is subsequently to use it, is inadmissible. However, not more than three blank forms of a kind, or three of each kind of dissimilar forms, may be included in a packet with a covering document which is itself admissible.

Yearly diaries are admitted, but diaries for shorter periods are inadmissible.

Blotting paper and similar substances are not regarded as ordinarily used for writing or printing and are inadmissible, but a single unfolded flat sheet of blotting paper and not sent as a sample, or one having affixed to it such an advertisement printed on ordinary paper or cardboard, is admitted in suitable open cover.

## PROHIBITED ARTICLES

Prohibited articles will be refused or detained. These may include:

- ✖ Certain circulars
- ✖ Fortune-telling Advertisements
- ✖ Lottery tickets
- ✖ Unsolicited circulars from money lenders

## DANGEROUS ARTICLES

Inflammable, noxious, corrosive, deleterious or otherwise harmful articles. Sharp instruments not properly packed. Improperly deactivated magical items of any kind. Matches of all kinds.

Hogswatch crackers are, however, permitted.

Any packet which is likely to pick a fight with or injure either other postal packets in the course of conveyance, or an Officer of the Post Office, or any other person who may deal with that packet.

## OTHER PROHIBITED ARTICLES

These would include:

✖ Contraband

✖ Counterfeit money or postage stamps (including stamps which, while formally printed for the Post Office, have for any reason been withdrawn e.g. the 'Lovers' stamp [see below]

✖ All animals, birds, fish and insects, with the exception of bees, leeches and silkworms

✖ Indecent, obscene or grossly offensive communications, marks, designs, prints, iconographs or other articles, unless they are sent stoutly sealed and have been counter-stamped by the Guild of Seamstresses

[Note 1: The Post Office is prepared to accept mail such as postcards, which conform to the categories of Naughty and Saucy, but draw the line at Rude.
Customers wishing to satisfy themselves on this score may, upon payment of a small sum, peruse the representative selection of all categories available on request at the Central Post Office.

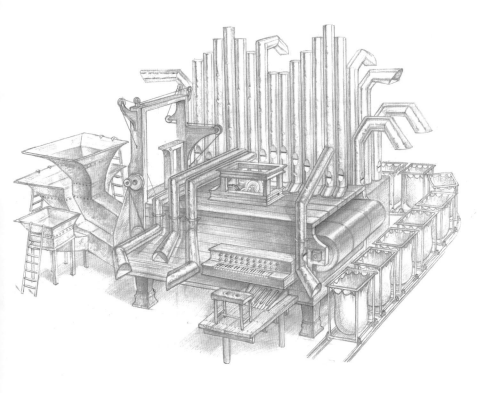

## THE 50P GREEN 2ND ISSUE STAMP (THE SO-CALLED 'LOVERS' STAMP): AN OFFICIAL STATEMENT.

There has been much scandalous talk about this stamp, which is now withdrawn. **THE FACTS** are as follows:

The Post Office commissioned a new painting for the 2nd Issue of this popular stamp, this time showing, at the suggestion of the Cabbage Growers' Association, a field of Micklegreen's Juicy, an improved variety, rather than that old stalwart, Autumn Reliant.

It just so happened that while our artist was working, a young man chose to use that field for the purpose of teaching a young lady to hoe. The arts of hoeing are of course much prized among the growers of the Plains, and a young woman who can turn her hand to the hoe, it is said, will never want for a husband.

It transpires that, whilst essaying a particularly tricky root aeration manoeuvre, the young woman noticed our artist and, overcome with maidenly modesty, mishandled the implement and caused both herself and her tutor to collapse among the brassicas, in, obviously, some considerable disarray, not to say déshabillé.

For his part, our artist, being city-born, was not to know that this was not just another agricultural procedure, and continued sketching in the belief that this would add 'colour' to the finished stamp. In this he was, we regret to say, prescient.

It was only after several hundred sheets of this stamp had been printed that it was put to our Officer in Charge of Stamps, Mr Stanley Howler, that those of a perverse and mischievous disposition might put a different, and we have to say, entirely unwarranted interpretation on the depiction. We are *assured* by more senior members of the Association that the young man was most probably demonstrating the fine old rural practice of 'shuggling', which is the warming of the seed-bed with the buttocks before sowing. It is good to see the old Traditions being passed on, and unfortunate that some people have used the Press to traduce them with questionable and not at all funny remarks.

Regrettably, a very few of the early run of the stamps also showed Lord Vetinari's head tilted slightly, as if he had decided to take an interest in bygone agricultural practices.

Because of the unwarranted assumptions made, this stamp was withdrawn and is not valid for use on letters. We are aware that a number of sheets have found their way into general circulation. If presented at a Post Office, they will be exchanged for stamps of the same value.

This unfortunate episode is closed.

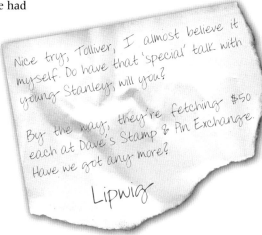

Nice try, Tolliver, I almost believe it myself. Do have that 'special' talk with young Stanley, will you?

By the way, they're fetching $50 each at Dave's Stamp & Pin Exchange. Have we got any more?

Lipwig

Stanley Howler

## EMBARRASSING PACKETS.

Packets embarrassing to the Post Office staff are also prohibited. Embarrassment may be caused by the method of addressing and the affixing of the stamp; the colour, type, shape and dimensions of the envelope.
Examples would be:

Addresses mis-spelled so as to give rise to a humorous double-entendre.

Stamps positioned adjacent or even above one another in such a way as to cause embarrassment, for example, the superimposition of the common One Penny stamp onto another denomination in such a way that Lord Vetinari appears to be sniffing the backside of a horse.

Any packet wrapped in such a way that it resembles certain private portions of the male human anatomy (specimens are on view to all male callers over the age of 21 and married female callers over the age of 30, by appointment).

## OFFENSIVE ACRONYMS and MISPLACED COSMETICS.

By custom and practice the acronyms SWALK, LANCRE and KLATCH are allowed on the reverse side of envelopes containing messages of a romantic nature.
HOWONDALAND, TWOSHIRTS and GENUA, however, are strictly forbidden, unless clearly part of the address. Anyone proposing any other acronym **MUST FIRST** show it to Miss Maccalariat, Head of Counter Services, who may approve it in the *extremely* unlikely event that no obscene or suggestive meaning can be determined.
While 'Sealed With A Loving Kiss' may well be romantic, customers should remember that a letter will share the postbag with many other letters, and both scent and lipstick are notoriously contagious in these circumstances. A letter between senior male business partners that reeks of *Nights of Passion* may cause unintended results. And, of course, lipstick in the wrong place is always difficult to explain away.

## PACKING AND MAKE-UP

Letters and postal packets of every kind must be so made up as to not only preserve the contents from loss or damage in the post, but also not to injure any other packets, or any Officer of the Post Office.

Miss Maccalariat

# PACKING REGULATIONS FOR CERTAIN ARTICLES

Any fragile article must be packed in a container of sufficient strength and surrounded in that container with sufficient soft material or wadding to protect the article from the effects of concussion, pressure and knocks to which postal packets are ordinarily exposed. The packet must bear the words **FRAGILE WITH CARE** written conspicuously on the face of the cover above the address, so that Postal Officers will know which packages will need to be tested to ensure that they can withstand dropping from great heights, stamping on, kicking, hitting with lump hammers, and any other normal treatment that would be given to such a package.

## BUTTER, CREAM AND OTHER SEMI-LIQUIDS

These and greasy or strong-smelling substances must be so packed that they will not soil or taint other packets. For example, a tightly lidded tin, secured with sealed string crossing the lid in two directions, then wrapped securely in greaseproof paper and placed in a well-constructed wooden box.

## EGGS

These are a challenge to the Postal Worker, and their safe transit cannot be guaranteed. If you want to risk it, you might try using a wooden box with suitable partitions and a well-fitting lid, wrapping each egg separately in newspaper or other soft material, placing the eggs on end, each in a separate partition, and filling up the vacant spaces in the box with newspaper or cotton waste. The parcel should be marked **EGGS** so that time is not wasted testing a parcel containing, say, rock samples.

## FISH AND OTHER MEAT

(Not including body parts travelling by mail between Igors; see below). These should be sewn into rush baskets, straw matting, sacking, or similar material, with sufficient internal waterproof wrapping or absorbent packing to prevent the contents from damaging or tainting the outer covering and thus making the parcels objectionable to handle for human Officers of the Post Office.

## LIQUIDS

These may be sent in tins or bottles (securely sealed). Containers of a pint or more must also be contained within a wooden box or wicker case, making good use of soft packaging to prevent damage in transit. Wow-Wow Sauce certified as less than five days old at the time of posting will be carried outside the coach at the discretion of the coachman, and only if the journey is expected to be not very bumpy. Wow-Wow Sauce aged five days and over is not allowed on Post Office premises or in Post Office vehicles .

## 'AIR POST'

The Post Office is pleased to announce a new service, to make the Grand Trunk Semaphore System more accessible by those uneasy with new technology.

Yes, letters that once would be carried by coach can now arrive in a matter of hours at destinations as far away as Uberwald!

The De Luxe Service is door-to-door. The letter will be collected by one of our nimble Semaphore Lads (the 'Speedies'), carried smartly though the most crowded of streets to the nearest semaphore tower, 'en-coded' and 'transmigrated' thence to the distant tower closest to the eventual destination, whence it is 'de-coded' and then delivered by messenger.

A tariff is available at most towers and all Post Offices.

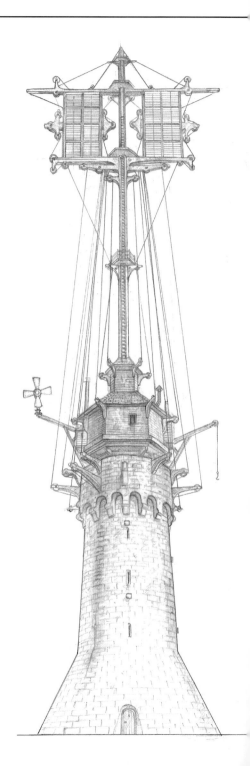

## IGOR2IGOR

Members of the Igor clan are invited to avail themselves of this Premium Service. The weekly Ankh-Morpork to Genua run, via Uberwald, can by arrangement take iceboxes big enough for most human organs in a capacious and very well insulated compartment. For those requiring a full, dedicated crypt-to-crypt service, call at the Central Post Office for our pamphlet 'Igor2 Igor: Foreign Parts Are Closer Than You Think!'

[Note 1: persons using the Igor2Igor service must ensure that the organs are in a strong icebox and, whenever possible, in a quiessant and non-aggressive state. This particularly applies to hands.]

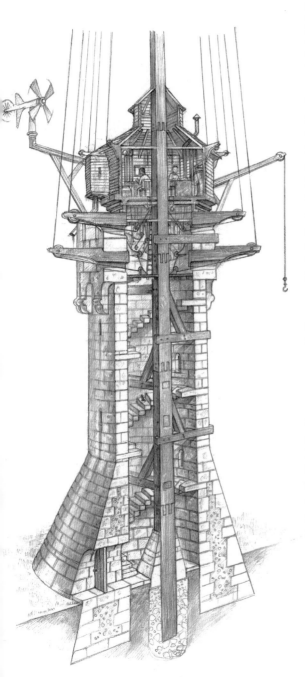

## SOIL OF THE HOMELAND BEING SHIPPED TO OR POSSIBLY CONTAINING CERTAIN CITIZENS OF UBERWALD

To be accepted in the Post, this must be enclosed in a secure wooden box, screwed down at no fewer than twelve-inch intervals and transported in such a way that it will be in transit only during the normal hours of daylight. Under no circumstances will such crates be accepted for transit by ship. Such crates must clearly be marked **NOT TO BE HANDLED DURING THE HOURS OF DARKNESS**.

[Note 1: Mail coaches travelling to or through Uberwald must carry Travelling Kit 3 (supplemental), comprising: one (1) flask Ecumenically Holy Water; two (2) stakes, wooden; one (1) hammer.]

[Note 2: The Soil of the Homeland Regulation applies only to those holding a valid membership of the Uberwald League of Temperance. Others attempting unfairly to obtain cheap travel by this means should be aware that the standard carrying box is fully airtight and is not opened en route, no matter how much hammering there is on the lid.]

## MOBILE POST OFFICES

These may be set up from time to time at major events for the sale of stamps, the franking of special covers, the sale of stamps, miscellaneous Post Office Services and, of course, the sale of stamps. Staff manning Mobile Post Offices will on demand produce their accreditation from the Postmaster General.

A small Mobile Post Office has been set up in Koom Valley for those citizens working or posted there during the current Truce and Negotiations. By Decree of Lord Vetinari, letters affixed with the new Koom Valley stamp will be delivered there at normal internal city rates.

## MAGIC ITEMS CARRIED BY THE POST

The Post Office has special rates for magical items carried in the mail.

Wizards' staffs will only be transported if accompanied by their owner.

Deactivated cauldrons, sealed potions, wands and pointy hats travel at normal parcel rates, as do (deactivated) broomsticks.

Activated broomsticks maintaining full lifting power will be carried free.

**1** New Year's Day
Holiday in UK

**Monday**

C & J left mid-morning.

**2** Bank Holiday in Scotland,
New Zealand

**Tuesday**

Matt. engineer turned up — no joy — left sub.
Matt.

**3**
○

**Wednesday**

**4**

**Thursday**

# Friday 5

# Saturday Epiphany 6

# Sunday 7

# Octeday

GREAT DATES IN POSTING
**3 January 1805.** The Post Office motto is installed on the front of the building. The motto was agreed upon following a competition amongst postal workers, narrowly beating its close rival 'WE'LL DELIVER IT IF WE FEEL LIKE IT AND NOT BEFORE'.

8        Monday

9        Tuesday

10        Wednesday

11        Thursday

# Friday 12

# Saturday 13

# Sunday 14

# Octeday

**TWOSHIRTS 2P CABBAGE FESTIVAL STAMP.**
Celebrates the Cabbage Macerating Festival in Twoshirts.
This stamp features a picture of two gentlemen treading
cabbages in a large vat.

**15** Martin Luther King
Day (USA)

**Monday**

**16**

**Tuesday**

**17**

**Wednesday**

**18**

**Thursday**

# Friday

# 19
●

# Saturday

Murharram
(Islamic New Year, 1428) **20**

# Sunday

# 21

# Octeday

HEROES OF THE POST OFFICE
Postmaster Norbert Anders was the man who came up with the slogan
'Post Early for Hogswatch'. He also came up with 'Always Use the Post
Code', although it was to be more than 140 years before anyone knew
what that one meant.

## 22                 Monday

Last gym session this afternoon.

## 23                 Tuesday

## 24                 Wednesday

## 25  Burns Night            Thursday

## Friday

Australia Day **26**

Applied for loan

## Saturday

Holocaust Memorial Day **27**

Returned loan papers

C arrived just before 6 pm.

## Sunday

**28**

C did all the little jobs. Late up so F
didn't get a walk till late. C ran us
to Ynys.

Sheryl's bike pinched from our front garden.

## Octeday

The Upwright Bros.

**29** Anniversary Day (NZ)         **Monday**

**30**         **Tuesday**

**31** C took me out for day. Went to **Wednesday**
Bettws y Coed. Had walk — didn't find Swallow Falls.
Lunch in Spinakes cafe + shopping i the souvenir
shops. On to Llangollen — walked up to Plas Newydd
for a look — gorgeous house and grounds, then
down into the town to the riverside. walk'd back
home by 6.35. Was sick twice — gong back to my
childhood car sickness.
Bought Bettina, C bought me a h'hog — Hoggarty

**1** Took 2 trips to Ynys with rubbish from **Thursday**
the outhouse. There is some floor space
out there now.

## Friday

C left 2pm-ish.

## Saturday 3

JAN, DAVE, SAM, SARAH & IAN CAME. JAN BROUGHT
MAIN COURSE — I FOUND DESSERT. SARAH HAS NEW
PUPPY — LUDO — SO FREYA HAD PLENTY OF EXERCISE
CHASING HIM ROUND

## Sunday

## Octeday

HEROES OF THE POST OFFICE
Temporary Hogswatch Postman Rodney Postlethwaite rescued his
mentor, Snr Postman Jess 'Jessica' Thrupp, from a nasty mauling
by two of Harry King's Lipwigzer dogs by belabouring the animals
about the head with a frozen leg of lamb he had been delivering to
the shop next door. He received the Post Man's Medal of Valour.

## 5                                         Monday

## 6    Ascension of Queen Elizabeth II <br>      Waitangi Day (NZ)                  Tuesday

## 7                                  Wednesday

## 8                                      Thursday

## Friday        9

## Saturday        10

## Sunday        11

## Octeday

Tolliver Groat

**12** Lincoln's Bithday (USA)　　　　　　　　　　　**Monday**

**13**　　　　　　　　　　　　　　　　**Tuesday**

**14** St Valentine's Day　　　　　　　　　**Wednesday**

**15** OT & SLING MAN — NOT GOOD NEWS　　**Thursday**
FOR CARERS.

# Friday
# 16

C ARRIVED V. LATE WITH KAREN — SEEMS
LIKEABLE. GOT THE BOOZE OUT (AND THE
PHOTOS)

# Saturday
# 17

Went out for meal at the host with C & K.
Very nice

# Sunday
# 18

Quinquagesima Sunday
Chinese New Year,
Year of the Pig

# Octeday

GREAT DATES IN POSTING
**13 February 1815.** The Post Master, Sir William Guilfoyle, introduces a pneumatic tube system to deliver money and change between the Cashier's Office and the front counters. Sadly, this had been designed by BS Johnson and, after a number of holes had been punched into the fabric of the building by supersonic tubes of small change, he was encouraged by the Patrician to suspend the system.

# 19          Monday

**20** Shrove Tuesday, Pancake Day,
Fat Tuesday, Mardi Gras (USA)      **Tuesday**

**21** Ash Wednesday      **Wednesday**

**22** Presidents' Day
George Washington's
Birthday (USA)      **Thursday**

## Friday
### 23

---

## Saturday
### 24

---

## Sunday
Quadragesima Sunday,
First Sunday in Lent
### 25

---

## Octeday

**THE PENNY PATRICIAN.** The first stamp produced by Messrs Teemer & Spools. It shows a fine burlage to the background over which is an engraved portrait of the Patrician. There is reputed to be a variation where the engraved plate was somehow damaged on part of the central image. This gave the appearance of some grey hair on the head of the Patrician. Once noticed, this particular issue was withdrawn and destroyed; however, a few stamps might be in the hands of some very careful and discreet collectors.

**26**                                Monday

**27**                                  Tuesday

**28**                              Wednesday

**1**   St David's Day                          Thursday

# Friday 2

# Saturday

Total Eclipse of the Moon
(21.30hrs-01.12hrs March 4) 3

# Sunday 4

Couldn't rouse Mum so had to call
ambulance. To Bangor. No-one seems
to know what's wrong.

# Octeday

GREAT DATES IN POSTING
**1 March 1888.** The Great Post Office Almost Robbery. Masked men, armed with pistol crossbows, entered the Mail Room at 02.45a.m. on the first of March. They overpowered the duty Post Man but, in their haste to pack as much Registered Mail as possible into their waiting cart, it seems that they fell into the Sorting Machine. They were subsequently arrested by Captain Vimes of the City Watch on 2 March 1983.

## 5 Monday
Labour Day
(Western Australia)

They think Mum has infection and should be in for a week.

## 6 Tuesday

Mum lost a lot of blood today — an ulcer had burst.

## 7 Wednesday

No change in Mum but still optimistic that they will discharge her soon.

## 8 Thursday

Chris & Jan managed to get to hospital this morning. Mum not really with them It appears she had a heart attack on Sat/Sun night. They are still optimistic.

## Friday 9

Mum now has pneumonia but they
still seem to be hopeful she can
get over it.
Chris, Becky came for the night.

## Saturday † 10

We went to hospital this morning. Jan +
Dave joined us. Mum unaware we were
there but seemed at peace. Left after
a few hours.

Phone call at midnight — Mum died.

## Sunday 11

Chris + Becky still with me as the
informing + sorting out begins

## Octeday

George Aggy

## 12  Commonwealth Day
Eight Hours Day (Tasmania)
**Monday**

## 13
**Tuesday**

## 14  Labour Day (Victoria)
**Wednesday**

## 15
**Thursday**

# Friday

# 16

# Saturday

St Patrick's Day **17**

Samedi Nuite Morte

# Sunday

Fourth Sunday in Lent
Mothering Sunday **18**

*Went to the hash for a meal.*

# Octeday

**HEROES OF THE POST OFFICE**
In 1737, Junior Postman Harold Pootah found, at the bottom of his mail sack, an envelope addressed to a Master James Shovel of 32b, Shamlegger Street. On arrival at this address, Mr Pootah found that the Shovel family had moved the day before to Genua. Not to be beaten, Jnr Pstmn Pootah set off, on foot, and – two and a half years later – delivered the letter to Master Shovel. When he got back to Ankh-Morpork, he was dismissed for being absent without leave. Three months later, a thank-you letter arrived from the Shovels but by then Harold Pootah had hanged himself – too ashamed to live on. He is the Post Office's only martyr. To date.

## 19 Monday

Holiday in N. Ireland, Eire
Canberra Day (ACT)
Partial Eclipse of the Sun (00.38hrs–04.25hrs)

Mum's funeral at Bangor Crematorium.
Wake at Malvern House. Pat & Frank,
Chris & Becky, Conrad & Karen stayed
night. Carers came for a drink (or two!)

## 20 Tuesday

Jan turned up this morning. Chaos all
round as everyone decided to throw
half the house away. Finally went
quiet after lunch when only C & K
were left.

## 21 Wednesday

Vernal Equinox
(Spring)

## 22 Thursday

C & K took me out to Anglesey for
the day. Had a nice time pootling
round & found nice pub for evening
meal.

# Friday 23

# Saturday 24

c o k went home early this evening.

# Sunday

British Summertime Begins 25

# Octeday

Mr Pony

**26**                                                      Monday

**27**                                                      Tuesday

**28**                                                      Wednesday

**29**                                                      Thursday

Jenny & Manda came round in the
evening — ended up as a booze-up!.

# Friday

# 30

# Saturday

Mawlid al-Nabi
(Muhammad's Birthday)

# 31

# Sunday

April Fool's Day
Palm/Passion Sunday
Daylight Savings Time starts (USA)

# 1

# Octeday

GREAT DATES IN POSTING
**1 April 1635.** Master Lambert Cordwainer becomes the first commoner customer of the new postal service. Master Cordwainer sent a letter to himself at his home address in order to 'teste thee system'. Cordwainer's original and unopened letter was recently sold on C-Bay for 150,000 AM$.

# 2

## Monday

○

## 3 Tuesday

Pesach (First Day of Passover)
Find a Rainbow Day

# 4

## Wednesday

## 5 Thursday

Maundy Thursday

Paid Phil £300 for roof - haven't seen him since

# Friday

Good Friday **6**

Heather came + did my feet

# Saturday

**7**

# Sunday

Easter Sunday **8**

Sheryl came round for an hour with Jess & Dan. Had migraine starting but think the pills have stopped it = hope. However, Freya has pulled a muscle or broken a rib on my left side again.

# Octeday

**HEROES OF THE POST OFFICE**
Postman Henry Sloop is the only Post Man on record to have delivered two hundred and forty-seven 'Sorry you were out' cards without ever once managing to deliver the parcel.

**9** Easter Monday                          **Monday**

Chest still hurting like hell.

**10**                                        **Tuesday**

**11**                           **Wednesday**

Roof done — so they say. Had to find
another £300 for them!

**12**                                    **Thursday**

Jenny & Nicky came round late afternoon
Wally rang
Pat rang — they're going on a cruise to
Iceland & Norway — lucky things

## Friday 13

Finally got house evaluation + claim to ISA.
Wallis away for another fortnight!.

## Saturday 14

Sheryl came lunchtime for rest of
sheets and a clematis

## Sunday 15

Low Sunday

Had good clear-out of Mum's drawers —
found her premium bonds!

## Octeday

Mr Spools

## 16 Monday

Met Nicky & Jenny outside NBS — Jenny now Entertainments Director at Hoten Dog!

Chat with Chris in evening

## 17 Tuesday

Met Nicky in woolies'. Sheryl & Jess in Park Road

Mandy dropped in in evening for chat + cuppa — someone's hacked into her account & half-inched her week's wages — the bastard!

## 18 Wednesday

Up early to walk dog. Hotpoint man didn't come till lunchtime but was here for over 2 hours! At least, I've got a washing-machine again. Started cataloguing books

## 19 Thursday

After a struggle, got some cash from machine for roofer. Apparently, my daily allowance is £200. Started on Mum's wardrobe — more diaries & other odd papers, booklets.

## Friday 20

Surprise, surprise! W/machine doesn't spin.
Wallie came for flying visit p.m. Sheryl came for
pencils — told me about Jenny's Helen.
Conrad & Karen arrived just before 1 am

## Saturday 21

The Queen's Birthday

Conrad took another load to dump.
C & Karen went out for rest of day
Jenny & Nicky came for about an hour
late afternoon

## Sunday 22

Earth Day

Three of us went out just after midday
up to own Nantool. Damp turning to heavy
rain just as we headed back to car.
C & K left 5.30ish — rang at 9.30 — good
time!

## Octeday

GREAT DATES IN POSTING
**16 April 1732.** Installation of the statue of the winged God in the
central concourse of the Ankh-Morpork Post Office. The statue is the
work of the great sculptor Auguste Buonarotti, who also carved the
cherubs and other gilded figures decorating the Opera House. The
winged God is believed to have been based upon the sculptor himself,
although this was disputed at the time by Signora Buonarotti.

## 23 St George's Day — Monday

Had a day doing nothing afte walking F.
We've got a new brown bin for green waste.
Sheryl came lunchtime re: gravel et.
Jenny came for an hour or so in the
early evening.

## 24 — Tuesday

## 25 ANZAC Day — Wednesday

Finally, the w/machine is working again!
Had Homeserve on 'phone for half-hour, sorting out
Ins. covers.
Cleared out my recipes

## 26 — Thursday

Cleared out my memento box

## Friday 27

Spent couple of hours at Jenny's midday —
met Abi.
Mr. Wallis rang when I got back. Probate papers —
the way — green light for shifting stuff.

## Saturday 28

Day of mourning for persons killed in the workplace

Creator's Birthday

Walked up town to look round 'Boot Sale' i
Youth Centre — too professional. Met Manda &
Sheryl there — walked back to footbridge with
them. Cleared the wardrobes this afternoon.
Rang Jan
Dylan returned Mum's bags from hospital

## Sunday 29

Very depressed all day, remembering Dad.

## Octeday

**HEROES OF THE POST OFFICE**
Counter Clerk Miss Alexandra Willett devised the system by which
customers needed to queue separately to purchase stamps, send a
parcel and renew a cart licence. This meant jobs for three staff when
previously only one was needed, and it greatly increased the confusion
of merged lines of customers in major Post Offices.

## 30 Beltane — Monday

Mr. Wallis rang — still sorting out papers.

## 1 — Tuesday
May Blossom Day

Papers came so booked appt. with solicitors in High St. for 12. Finally got some attention after half-an hour. Posted the lot back to Wallis Recorded del. or something. Spent afternoon hacking at bottom hedge — with audience — those kids never seemed to be inside in hot weather.

## 2 — Wednesday

○ Stiffness after yesterday only crept up on me during day. Assaulted Xmas decorations, then my kitchen cupboard. Nothing much left now — most out of date a in bin

## 3 4 — Thursday
Friday →
(See Friday)

### Friday ~~Thursday~~ Up at 7 am 3 /4

C & D came to do Conrad's window lock – also
sorted out back door problem – adjust a screw!
Voted – see halo! Met Jeanny then went back to
beach with Freya, who vanished. Met her
coming across by Minny-Mor, looking very sheepish.
Assaulted downstairs kitchen cupboards

### Saturday — Cinco de Mayo 5

### Sunday 6

### Octeday

The town of Bad Blinz, a great tourist centre and famed as the town that made a pact with a clan of intelligent rats, has issued stamps in the following values: 1 blzot (Brown, showing a smiling rat); 2 blzot (Red, a view of the Rathaus); 5 blzot (Blue, The Rat Piper); 10 blzot (Black, The Ratcatcher Museum); 20 blzot (Green, The Rat Clock) 50 blzot (four-colour, The Dancing Rats), and the 100 blzot (four colour, showing a representation of Wotua Gram's famous painting 'The Signing Of The Pact'). In the interests of equality among all its citizens, Bad Blinz has also issued miniature stamps for the use of the rat population, which are of great interest to the collector.

**7** May Bank Holiday (UK)
Labour Day (Queensland)    **Monday**

**8**    **Tuesday**

**9**    **Wednesday**

**10**    **Thursday**

# Friday 11

# Saturday 12

# Sunday 13

Rogation Sunday
Mother's Day (USA,
Canada, Australia & NZ)

# Octeday

GREAT DATES IN POSTING
**16 May 1978.** The first 'Mail Order' service is set up by Mr CMOT
Dibbler, a tradesperson of Ankh-Morpork. Despite the name, Mr
Dibbler's service also extended to sheet-armour.

**14**          Monday

**15**          Tuesday

**16**
●          Wednesday

**17**   Ascension Day
       Holy Thursday          Thursday

# Friday 18

# Saturday

Armed Forces Day **19**

# Sunday 20

# Octeday

GREAT DATES IN POSTING

**17 May 1978.** The first 'Mail Order' service is closed down  by Lord Vetinari, who does not approve of the use of 'punes' or plays on words in the mission statements of city businesses.

**21** Victoria Day (Canada)
Adelaide Cup Day (SA)  **Monday**

**22**  **Tuesday**

**23** Shavuot
(Feast of Weeks)  **Wednesday**

**24**  **Thursday**

# Friday

## 25

Wear lilac if you were there

# Saturday

## 26

# Sunday

Pentecost
Whit Sunday **27**

# Octeday

HEROES OF THE POST OFFICE
Post Master General Elwes is credited with being the man who
introduced the queuing system into the Ankh-Morpork Post Office. In
the 25 years prior to that innovation, twelve people had died fighting
to send a postal packet and one person lost the use of a leg in an effort
to hand in a delayed tax return.

**28** Spring Bank Holiday
Memorial Day (USA)                                    **Monday**

**29**                                                **Tuesday**

**30**                                                **Wednesday**

**31**                                                **Thursday**

# Friday

1
○

# Saturday

Coronation Day

2

# Sunday

Trinity Sunday

3

# Octeday

GREAT DATES IN POSTING
**31 May 1798.** The rules for the operation of Sub-post Offices were relaxed to permit the sale, on the premises, of a range of grocery produce but also including stationery items, hair grips, sink plugs, hair combs and novelty false nose/moustache sets.

**4** Foundation Day (WA)
The Queen's Official Birthday (NZ)

## Monday

**5**

## Tuesday

**6**

## Wednesday

**7** Corpus Christi

## Thursday

Finder's Day

# Friday 8

# Saturday 9

The Queen's
Official Birthday

# Sunday 10

Birthday of Prince Philip,
Duke of Edinburgh

# Octeday

Senior Post Man Bates

**11** The Queen's Official Birthday
(Australia except WA)

**Monday**

**12**

**Tuesday**

**13**

**Wednesday**

**14** Flag Day (USA)

**Thursday**

# Friday

**15**
●

---

# Saturday

**16**

---

# Sunday

Fathers' Day (USA,
Canada, Australia & NZ) **17**

---

# Octeday

Adora Belle Dearheart

**18** Waterloo Day

# Monday
Small Gods' Eve

**19** Juneteenth (Liberation
of Slaves Day, USA)

# Tuesday
Small Gods' Day

**20**

# Wednesday

**21** Longest day of the year
Litha (Summer Solstice)

# Thursday

# Friday

**22**

# Saturday

**23**

# Sunday

St Jean-Baptiste Day **24**

Treacle Pie Day

# Octeday

**HEROES OF THE POST OFFICE**
Miss Honoria Maccalariat (an ancestor of our
current Post Office colleague) saved the Post
Office thousands of dollars when she suggested
that the pens should be chained to the counter.

## 25           Monday

## 26           Tuesday

## 27           Wednesday

## 28           Thursday

## Friday

# 29

## Saturday

# 30
○

Wizards' Excuse-Me

## Sunday

Canada Day

# 1

## Octeday

Crispin Horsefry

## 2     Monday

## 3     Tuesday

## 4    Independence Day (USA)    Wednesday

## 5     Thursday

# Friday 6
Patrician's Day

# Saturday 7

# Sunday 8

# Octeday

POSTAL PASSENGERS

Passengers on the Mail Coach are Permitted to Carry no More than Fourteen Pounds in Weight, at a Cost of One Penny per Pound, plus One Dollar for their own Fare. Such Weight May Not Include Items of a Noxious Nature (Decomposing Bodies, Bananas*, Tuna Sandwiches) nor any Item, any Dimension of Which Exceeds Two Feet Three Inches (2'3").

[*this rule has now been amended to exclude bananas, since the date of the UU Librarian becoming an orang-utan]

# 9            Monday

# 10           Tuesday

# 11          Wednesday

# 12    Battle of the Boyne (Holiday in N. Ireland)      Thursday

# Friday
## 13

# Saturday
Bastille Day
## 14
●

# Sunday
## 15

# Octeday

GREAT DATES IN POSTING
**18 July 1798.** Publication of the Fourteenth Edition of the Post Office Regulations. Known to bibliophiles as the 'Tiny Post Book' because of a typographical error on page 127, so that the rules stated: 'Envelopes less than four inches (4″) in length by two and three-quarter inches (2 3/4″) in width must be used.' The omission of the word 'not' led to the Broad Way Post Office being presented with more than two thousand letters measuring around one inch (1″) by half an inch (1/2″) before the edition could be recalled and corrected.

# 16
## Monday

# 17
## Tuesday

# 18
## Wednesday

# 19
## Thursday

# Friday 20

# Saturday 21

# Sunday 22

Uberwald League of Temperance Day:
Remember: Not One Drop!

# Octeday

GREAT DATES IN POSTING
**24 July 1797.** The Post Office welcomes its One Millionth Customer, Mrs Sylvestra Wincot. She is presented with a dozen pre-stamped envelopes, an engraving of the then Post Master (Mr N. Aushilfe) and a souvenir bottle of blue-black ink.

23          Monday

24          Tuesday

25          Wednesday

26          Thursday

# Friday 27

# Saturday 28

de Murforte Day

# Sunday 29

Mizzling Sunday

# Octeday

GREAT DATES IN POSTING
**25 Grune 1722.** Master Richard Scallion is the youngest person ever to be dismissed from the Postal Service, for writing 'Oh Yes They Do' on a package for the Duke of Eorle bearing the inscription 'PRICELESS ENGRAVINGS – DO NOT BEND'.

## 30 Monday
○

## 31 Tuesday

## 1 Wednesday
Lammas
(Lughnasadh)

## 2 Thursday

# Friday 3

# Saturday 4

# Sunday 5

# Octeday

HEROES OF THE POST OFFICE
Counter Clerk Miss Amelie Willett introduced the idea that Post Office
forms should be revised on a daily basis, to ensure that once a
customer reached the counter, they would almost certainly have the
wrong form and would have to go back to the start of the queue.

**6** Picnic Day, Holiday in
Scotland, Republic of
Ireland, Canada & Australia

**Monday**

**7** **Tuesday**

**8** **Wednesday**

**9** **Thursday**

# Friday 10

# Saturday 11

# Sunday 12

# Octeday

Mrs Cake

## 13          Monday

## 14          Tuesday

## 15    Assumption of the Virgin Mary      Wednesday

## 16          Thursday

# Friday 17

# Saturday 18

# Sunday 19

# Octeday

Mr Pump

**20**                                Monday

**21**                                 Tuesday

**22**                               Wednesday

**23**                                Thursday

# Friday

# 24

# Saturday

# 25

# Sunday

# 26

Head of the River: running
race with boats on the Ankh

# Octeday

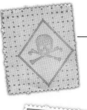

**THE ASSASSINS' GUILD THREE PENCE STAMP** was issued after problems
with the gum on the Assassins' Post-Paid. This latter stamp, known as the Zombie
Stamp, or Thrup'ny Dreadful, was withdrawn after unsubstantiated rumours that
the Guild was using its stamps to poison 'clients'. After the outcry and a possibly
coincidental funeral, the remaining Post-Paid stamps were withdrawn. A few
stamps have found their way onto the market and are of interest to collectors. A
sealed transparent envelope is advised.

**27** Summer Bank Holiday

**Monday**

Brebb & Leppis Day

**28** Total Eclipse of the Moon
(08.51hrs-12.24hrs)

○

**Tuesday**

**29**

**Wednesday**

**30**

**Thursday**

Friday                                                    31

Saturday                                                  1

Sunday                                                    2

Octeday

GREAT DATES IN POSTING
**27 August 1650.** Nine forty-five a.m. First letter delivered to Genua
from Ankh-Morpork by the King's Letter Office, having been handed
in to the office on Broad Way at twelve minutes past three on the
afternoon of 23 August 1649.

**3**    Labour Day (Canada & USA)                         **Monday**

Witch Trials

**4**                                           **Tuesday**

**5**                                      **Wednesday**

**6**                                        **Thursday**

# Friday 7

# Saturday 8

# Sunday 9

# Octeday

HEROES OF THE POST OFFICE
There is a plaque to the memory of Sir Arthur Brady, the Morporkian composer who, in 1649, wrote the Post Horn tunes which have been used ever since by the mail coachmen. These include 'Express Mail Coming Through', 'Runaway Horses' and 'Make Sure There's a Clear Path to the Privy When We Draw Up'. Sir Arthur's only other well-known tune is the backing to the famous Omnian hymn 'Om is Crushing the Infidel with Large Rocks'.

## 10 Monday
UU Rag Week

**11** Partial Eclipse of the Sun
(10.27hrs-14.37hrs)

## Tuesday

## 12 Wednesday

**13** Rosh Hashanah (Jewish New Year)
First Day of Ramadân

## Thursday

Friday **14**

Saturday Battle of Britain Day **15**

Sunday **16**

Octeday

**17** Monday

**18** Tuesday

**19** Wednesday

**20** Thursday

# Friday

**21**

# Saturday

Yom Kippur
(Day of Atonement) **22**

# Sunday

Mabon
(Autumn Equinox) **23**

# Octeday

Gladys

**24** Monday

**25** Tuesday

**26** Wednesday
○

**27** Succoth
(First Day of Tabernacles) Thursday

# Friday 28

# Saturday 29

# Sunday 30

# Octeday

GREAT DATES IN POSTING
**1 October 1900.** Tailcoats cease to be a part of the Postal uniform when the first female Postal Delivery Operatives are employed. The only exception is the frock-coat still worn on ceremonial occasions by the Post Masters.

**1** The Queen's Official Birthday (Western Australia)
Labour Day (NSW, ACT, SA)    **Monday**

**2**    **Tuesday**

**3**    **Wednesday**

**4**    **Thursday**

# Friday 5

# Saturday 6

# Sunday 7

# Octeday

GREAT DATES IN POSTING
**4 October 1530.** Sir Rolande de Colline appointed as the first Ankh-Morpork Master of the Posts, with a salary of three shillings a month, plus two rabbits, a pound of turnips and a flagon and a half of ale.

**8**   Thanksgiving Day (Canada)
Columbus Day (USA)

## Monday

**9**

## Tuesday

**10**

## Wednesday

**11**
●

## Thursday

# Friday

Chase Whiskers Day

Eid al-Fitr
(Ramadân ends) **12**

# Saturday

**13**

# Sunday

**14**

# Octeday

**HEROES OF THE POST OFFICE**
On 15 Sektober 1841, Snr Postman Granville Roberts was delivering a parcel to Sir Despard Pontefract at his home in Scoone Avenue, when one of Sir Despard's hounds, Saliva, ran into him, causing him to lose his grip on the package, which was marked 'Extremely Fragile'. Roberts threw himself full length to the floor to catch the parcel (containing, as we now know, an almost priceless cut-crystal decanter attributed to Vermicelli). In doing so, he landed on the dog, Saliva, who sank his fangs into Postman Roberts' leg. Despite the pain, Roberts saved the parcel and dragged the dog (still attached to his leg) up the 200-yard drive to the front door, where he handed the package to the Pontefracts' butler before collapsing from loss of blood.

**15**                     **Monday**

**16**   Bosses' Day             **Tuesday**

**17**               **Wednesday**

B.E. Day

**18**                 **Thursday**

## Friday

**19**

---

## Saturday

Sweetest Day **20**

---

## Sunday

Sto Plains Tiddly-Winks Finals

202nd Anniversary of the
Battle of Trafalgar **21**

---

## Octeday

Rats have only a limited use for currency, but extremely small gold, silver and bronze coins have been minted and are known respectively as the Candle, the Medium Potato and the Raisin. Rat stamps to the same values are printed and paw-perforated by the rats themselves. All three are coloured red, brown and black, and show the relevant object and the phrase 'Rattus Sapiens' in human and rat scripts. They are on sale in Bad Blintz Post Office. The Raisin, Medium Potato and Candle stamps are equivalent to the Bad Blintz 'human' 1, 5 and 20 blzot stamps.

**22** Labour Day (NZ)

# Monday

**23**

# Tuesday
Soul Cake Tuesday

**24**

# Wednesday
Soul Cake Day

**25**

# Thursday
Soul Cake Day

# Friday

Alfred the Great's
Day **26**

○

---

# Saturday

**27**

---

# Sunday

British Summertime ends
Daylight Savings Time ends (USA) **28**

---

# Octeday

**TOWER OF ART.** Depicting the Unseen University Tower of Art amid its scholastic environment. A most unusual stamp with reports of transfiguration within the engraving. The first transfiguration is where the bird to the right of the tower is replaced by a man in free fall. The second inexplicable transfiguration is a small splash visible in the water near the base of the tower.

# 29             Monday

# 30             Tuesday

# 31   Hallowe'en        Wednesday
Samhain

# 1   All Saints' Day        Thursday

# Friday

All Souls' Day **2**

# Saturday

**3**

# Sunday

**4**

# Octeday

GREAT DATES IN POSTING

**30 Sektober 1635.** Installation of the first official Post Office Cat. Known as 'Mr Tiddles', the cat remained in office for an amazing twenty-three years, during which time the CatLog shows he killed 1,137 rats, 1,563 mice and voles, 212 small birds, and one junior Post Man (the cat dislodged a piece of loose masonry which fell on the unfortunate Mr Trinder).

Mr Tiddles

5 Guy Fawkes' Day                                   **Monday**

6 Melbourne Cup Day
  (Australia)                                        **Tuesday**

7
●                                                    **Wednesday**

8                                                    **Thursday**

# Friday

Diwali **9**

# Saturday

**10**

# Sunday

Remembrance Sunday
Remembrance Day (Canada)
Veterans' Day (USA) **11**

# Octeday

HEROES OF THE POST OFFICE
Jedediah Berk, of the Guild of Alchemists, became the unsung hero of generations of Post Mistresses and Counter Clerks in the Package Repair Office when he invented the rubber roller in a small trough of green, smelly water – a device which liberated them from having to lick miles of brown sticky tape each Hogswatch, mending badly constructed parcels. The glue on the government-issued tape is a compound of boiled slugs and horse bones.

12                                                 **Monday**

13                                                 **Tuesday**

14    Birthday of the Prince of Wales                  **Wednesday**

15                                                 **Thursday**

# Friday

**16**

# Saturday

**17**

# Sunday

**18**

# Octeday

Extremely Senior Post Man Anghammarad

# 19
## Monday
Tattogey Week

# 20
## Tuesday

# 21
## Wednesday

# 22
Thanksgiving Day
(USA)
## Thursday

# Friday 23

# Saturday 24
○

# Sunday 25

# Octeday

GREAT DATES IN POSTING
**21 November 1878.** First performance of the Disc's first Postal Opera, 'Die Postmeistersinger von Uberwald'. This was a massive success and played to packed houses until it was ousted in popular appeal some two years later by the even more popular 'Das Zaubebriefmarkenalbum'.

**26** Monday

**27** Tuesday

**28** Wednesday

**29** Thursday

Friday                                    St Andrew's Day  30

Saturday                                                  1

Sunday                                    Advent Sunday    2

Octeday

Jimmy Tropes

## 3 Monday

## 4 Tuesday

## 5 Wednesday

## 6 Thursday

# Friday                                               7

# Saturday                    Immaculate Conception    8

# Sunday                      Second Sunday in Advent   9
●

# Octeday

HEROES OF THE POST OFFICE
Robert Hummingbird, a clerk in the Central Ankh-Morpork Post
Office, was the person who thought of filling the handle of the
'FRAGILE' stamp with lead shot, to give it greater ability to make
an impression.

**10**                                         Monday

**11**                                           Tuesday

**12**                                      Wednesday

**13**                                         Thursday

# Friday                                              14

# Saturday                                            15

# Sunday                        Third Sunday in Advent 16

# Octeday

GREAT DATES IN POSTING
**12 December 1876.** Delivery of the first stocks of rubber finger stalls, following the death of a Counter Clerk who had licked his fingers to turn the pages of a book being delivered to a local Monastery.

# 17                         Monday

# 18                          Tuesday

# 19                     Wednesday

# 20  Eid al-Adha                  Thursday
(Festival of Sacrifice)

# Friday

## 21

# Saturday

Yule (Winter Solstice)
Shortest Day of the Year

## 22

# Sunday

Fourth Sunday in Advent

## 23

# Octeday

GREAT DATES IN POSTING
**13 January 1877.** Mr William Sonkey personally replaces the delivery with the correct rubber product following complaints from female Counter staff.

**24** Christmas Eve            **Monday**

○

---

**25** Christmas Day            **Tuesday**

---

**26** Boxing Day
St Stephen's Day          **Wednesday**
Proclamation Day (SA)

---

**27**            **Thursday**

# Friday 28

# Saturday 29

# Sunday 30
Hogswatcheve

# Octeday

GREAT DATES IN POSTING

**27 December 1762.** Publication of the First Edition of the Post Office Regulations. Previously, these had been handed down by a combination of oral tradition and a large box-file stuffed with Royal Commands and letters from Head Office.

31 New Year's Eve

**Monday**
Hogswatchnight

ICK

**Tuesday**
Hogswatchday

First published in Great Britain in 2006 by Victor Gollancz Ltd
A member of the Orion Publishing Group, Orion House, 5 Upper St Martin's Lane, London WC2H 9EA
Text © 2006 Terry and Lyn Pratchett, and Stephen Briggs
Illustrations © 2006 Paul Kidby
Discworld® is a trade mark registered by Terry Pratchett.
All rights reserved.
The right of Terry Pratchett and Stephen Briggs to be identified as authors of this work
has been asserted by them under the Copyright, Designs and Patents Act, 1988.
ISBN 0 575 07723 9
Printed and bound in Italy

The publishers have taken every care in the preparation of the information contained
in this diary but cannot be held responsible for the consequences of any inaccuracies.

# YEAR PLANNER 2008

| | January | February | March | April | May | June |
|------|---------|----------|-------|-------|-----|------|
| Mon | | | | | | |
| Tues | 1 | | | 1 | | |
| Wed | 2 | | | 2 | | |
| Thu | 3 | | | 3 | 1 | |
| Fri | 4 | 1 | | 4 | 2 | |
| Sat | 5 | 2 | 1 | 5 | 3 | |
| Sun | 6 | 3 | 2 | 6 | 4 | 1 |
| Mon | 7 | 4 | 3 | 7 | 5 | 2 |
| Tues | 8 | 5 | 4 | 8 | 6 | 3 |
| Wed | 9 | 6 | 5 | 9 | 7 | 4 |
| Thu | 10 | 7 | 6 | 10 | 8 | 5 |
| Fri | 11 | 8 | 7 | 11 | 9 | 6 |
| Sat | 12 | 9 | 8 | 12 | 10 | 7 |
| Sun | 13 | 10 | 9 | 13 | 11 | 8 |
| Mon | 14 | 11 | 10 | 14 | 12 | 9 |
| Tues | 15 | 12 | 11 | 15 | 13 | 10 |
| Wed | 16 | 13 | 12 | 16 | 14 | 11 |
| Thu | 17 | 14 | 13 | 17 | 15 | 12 |
| Fri | 18 | 15 | 14 | 18 | 16 | 13 |
| Sat | 19 | 16 | 15 | 19 | 17 | 14 |
| Sun | 20 | 17 | 16 | 20 | 18 | 15 |
| Mon | 21 | 18 | 17 | 21 | 19 | 16 |
| Tues | 22 | 19 | 18 | 22 | 20 | 17 |
| Wed | 23 | 20 | 19 | 23 | 21 | 18 |
| Thu | 24 | 21 | 20 | 24 | 22 | 19 |
| Fri | 25 | 22 | 21 | 25 | 23 | 20 |
| Sat | 26 | 23 | 22 | 26 | 24 | 21 |
| Sun | 27 | 24 | 23 | 27 | 25 | 22 |
| Mon | 28 | 25 | 24 | 28 | 26 | 23 |
| Tues | 29 | 26 | 25 | 29 | 27 | 24 |
| Wed | 30 | 27 | 26 | 30 | 28 | 25 |
| Thu | 31 | 28 | 27 | | 29 | 26 |
| Fri | | 29 | 28 | | 30 | 27 |
| Sat | | | 29 | | 31 | 28 |
| Sun | | | 30 | | | 29 |
| Mon | | | 31 | | | 30 |
| Tues | | | | | | |

| Offle | February | March | April | May | June |
|-------|----------|-------|-------|-----|------|